ROCKS
and
LANDSCAPE
of the North York Moors

Photograph acknowledgements

Chris Ceaser: Front cover (bottom), 22, 38 (top)

Mike Kipling: Front cover (top left), 2, 3, 4 (bottom), 5 (bottom), 11 (centre right), 16 (top), 19 (top), 24 (both), 28 (left), 29 (top left), 30 (top left and right), 36 (top), 42 (top), 43 (top), back cover

Mark Denton: 12 (top), 18

Peter Wilson: 25 (bottom)

Andy Elliot: 28 (right)

Page 39: Photographs of Rosedale workings and Ingleby Incline reproduced by kind permission of Beck Isle Museum.

All other photographs are by the author or from the North York Moors National Park Authority collection. If we have unknowingly missed any photographer's credit, please accept our apologies and contact the publisher.

The maps and sections in this volume are based upon British Geological Survey 1:50,000 Provisional Series, Sheets 34, 35, 42, 43, 44, 52, 53, 54 and 1:250,000 Series, Sheet 54N 02W Tyne Tees, Solid Geology, with the permission of the British Geological Survey. Reproduced by permission of the British Geological Survey. © NERC. All rights reserved. IPR/128-50C

All illustrations copyright © Alan Marshall 2010

First published by North York Moors National Park Authority, 2010

North York Moors National Park Authority
The Old Vicarage
Bondgate
Helmsley
York YO62 5BP
Tel 01439 770657

A CIP catalogue record for this book is available from the British Library

ISBN 978-1-904622-24-6

Designed by Alan Marshall/Heron Recreations
Illustrations by Alan Marshall/Heron Recreations

Printed and bound in Great Britain by Falcon Press, Stockton-on-Tees

ROCKS
and
LANDSCAPE
of the North York Moors

Roger Osborne

Illustrations by Alan Marshall

CONTENTS

Rocks and Landscape of the North York Moors 6
Geology map and section 7
Landscape and Rocks in 3D 8

Sutton Bank 10
Bilsdale and the Hambleton Hills 12
Kilburn and the Southwest 14
Cleveland Hills 16
Roseberry Topping 18
Upper Eskdale 20
Lower Eskdale 22

The Northern Dales 24
Cliffs and Coves 26
Coastal Plain 28

High Moors 30
Slacks and Swangs on the High Moorland 32
Cleveland Dyke 34
Newtondale 36
Rosedale Ironstone 38

The Tabular Hills 40
Hole of Horcum and Levisham Moor 42
Dales of the Tabular Hills 44
Forge Valley and Hackness 46

Useful information 48

Rocks and Landscape of the North York Moors

The North York Moors have long been a magnet for nature-lovers and walkers. But they also have a strong claim to be at the historic heart of the study of landscape and rocks. The rocks of this area have produced one of the most spectacular landscapes in England. It is the wonderful exposures of Jurassic rock on the moors and coast that have drawn a succession of geologists, from William Smith in the 1820s onwards, to northeast Yorkshire. You don't need to be an expert to get pleasure and understanding from this book, but you will be following in some eminent footsteps.

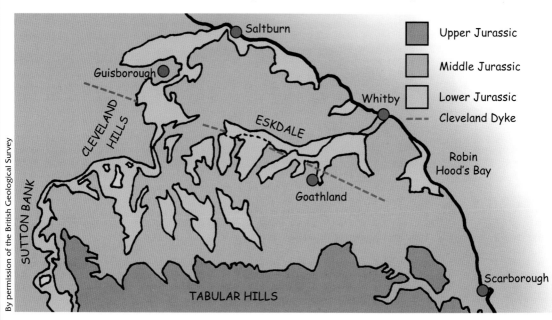

By permission of the British Geological Survey

Knowing more about how the rocks and landscape fit together will give you a better understanding of the North York Moors and will make your experience of this beautiful landscape even more enjoyable. This book is written for general readers with an interest in the great outdoors, and we use lots of photographs and illustrations to guide you to a richer understanding of the moors and dales.

Underlying every feature of the landscape is its geology - both the different types of rock that lie beneath the ground, and the ice and water that have worked on the rocks to develop such a unique and spectacular landscape. The basic structure of the North York Moors is fairly simple, with a series of rock layers lying on top of each other and sloping gently towards the south, as in the section below.

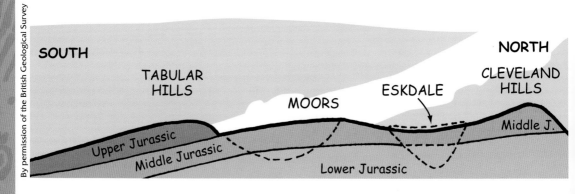

By permission of the British Geological Survey

How to use this book

One reason why people come to study rocks here is that the structure is fairly simple to understand. The Jurassic rocks lie on top of each other in an orderly sequence. Throughout this book we use maps and sections to show where these layers come to the surface, and how they affect the landscape. The drawing overleaf gives a useful summary.

The drawing on the right is a complete geological column of rocks in the North York Moors National Park. The oldest, Redcar Mudstone is at the bottom - this is around 200 million years old. The youngest, Upper Calcareous Grit, which is about 150 million years old is at the top. You will see these rocks marked on maps and sections on the following pages; this column is a handy reference for you to see whereabouts a particular landform is in the geological succession.

So, for example, on page 17 the section shows how the north face of the Cleveland Hills is made of layers of Middle Jurassic and Lower Jurassic rock. Remember that the older rocks are always lower down - the sequence stays in the same order everywhere. As you look at the drawings you will begin to see how the maps and sections work together and how they reveal the geological structure.

Use these pages and the diagram overleaf as your reference points and you will find the rocks of the moors give an extra dimension to your enjoyment of the landscape.

One last thing - don't forget that the area has two of the finest collections of Jurassic fossils in the country, at Whitby Museum and the Rotunda Museum in Scarborough. Full details are on page 48.

By permission of the British Geological Survey

Upper Calcareous Grit (UCG)	Upper Jurassic
Malton Oolite (MaO)	
Middle Calcareous Grit (MCG)	
Hambleton Oolite (HaO)	
Passage Beds (PaB)	
Lower Calcareous Grit (LCG)	
Oxford Clay (OxC)	
Osgodby sandstone (Osy)	Middle Jurassic (MJ)
Cornbrash (Cb)	
Long Nab (LoN)	
Moor Grit (MrG)	
Scarborough Limestone (Scr)	
Cloughton Formation (ClF)	
Saltwick (Swk)	
Dogger (Dgr)	Lower Jurassic
Whitby Mudstone (WhM) (inc. Alum and Jet Rock)	
Cleveland Ironstone (CdI)	
Staithes Sandstone (Sta)	
Redcar Mudstone (ReM)	

Landscape and Rocks in 3D

The North York Moors are built on a stack of Jurassic rocks that slope gradually towards the south. The key rock bed is the Middle Jurassic layer of sandstone, mudstone, limestone and grit (175 to 160 million years old), marked as green on the section, which lies beneath the central and northern moorland and the Cleveland Hills. On the section the Middle Jurassic beds are combined into one layer.

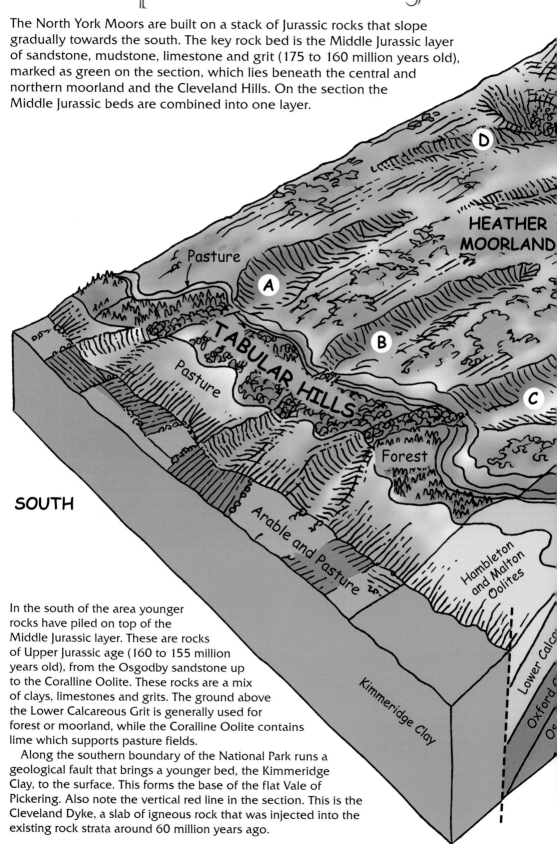

HEATHER MOORLAND

Pasture

TABULAR HILLS

Pasture

Forest

Arable and Pasture

SOUTH

Hambleton and Malton Oolites

Kimmeridge Clay

Lower Calca

Oxford

Os

In the south of the area younger rocks have piled on top of the Middle Jurassic layer. These are rocks of Upper Jurassic age (160 to 155 million years old), from the Osgodby sandstone up to the Coralline Oolite. These rocks are a mix of clays, limestones and grits. The ground above the Lower Calcareous Grit is generally used for forest or moorland, while the Coralline Oolite contains lime which supports pasture fields.

Along the southern boundary of the National Park runs a geological fault that brings a younger bed, the Kimmeridge Clay, to the surface. This forms the base of the flat Vale of Pickering. Also note the vertical red line in the section. This is the Cleveland Dyke, a slab of igneous rock that was injected into the existing rock strata around 60 million years ago.

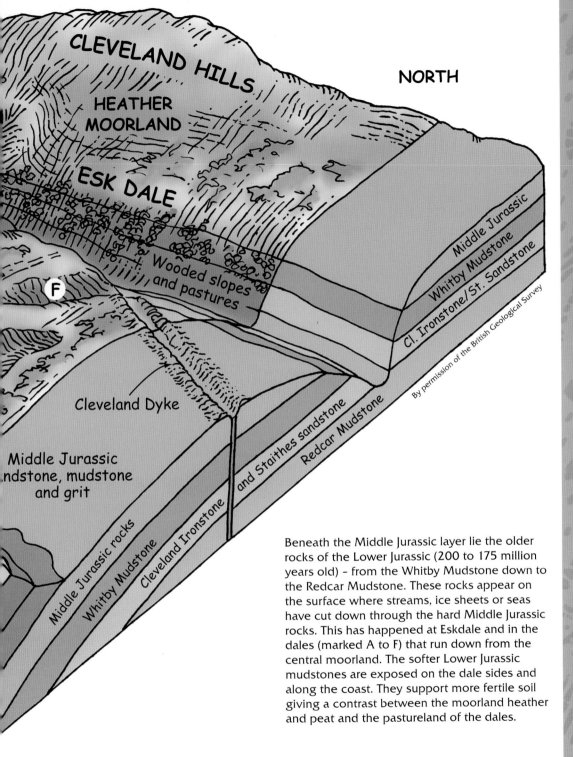

CLEVELAND HILLS

HEATHER MOORLAND

ESK DALE

Wooded slopes and pastures

F

NORTH

Middle Jurassic

Whitby Mudstone

Cl. Ironstone/St. Sandstone

By permission of the British Geological Survey

Cleveland Dyke

and Staithes sandstone

Redcar Mudstone

Middle Jurassic ndstone, mudstone and grit

Middle Jurassic rocks

Whitby Mudstone

Cleveland Ironstone

Beneath the Middle Jurassic layer lie the older rocks of the Lower Jurassic (200 to 175 million years old) - from the Whitby Mudstone down to the Redcar Mudstone. These rocks appear on the surface where streams, ice sheets or seas have cut down through the hard Middle Jurassic rocks. This has happened at Eskdale and in the dales (marked A to F) that run down from the central moorland. The softer Lower Jurassic mudstones are exposed on the dale sides and along the coast. They support more fertile soil giving a contrast between the moorland heather and peat and the pastureland of the dales.

Sutton Bank

Sutton Bank is a wonderful place to start our exploration of the rocks and landscape of the North York Moors. The western escarpment marks the edge of the National Park and is one of the most spectacular inland cliffs in England. The cliff is there because the land to the east - the upland area of the moors - was lifted up during the last fifty million years. The low land to the west was later invaded by a series of ice sheets. The edges of ice sheets are packed with rock fragments and have immense power to grind through the surrounding land. Here the ice sheet sheered off a near-vertical cliff around 200 metres high as it travelled south.

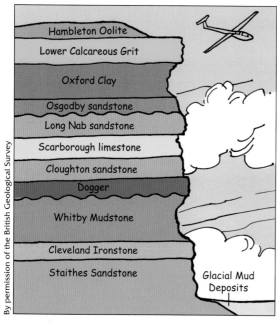

Hambleton Oolite

Lower Calcareous Grit

Oxford Clay

Osgodby sandstone

Long Nab sandstone

Scarborough limestone

Cloughton sandstone

Dogger

Whitby Mudstone

Cleveland Ironstone

Staithes Sandstone

Glacial Mud Deposits

The cliff at Sutton Bank shows a slice through much of the Jurassic sequence of rocks. The Hambleton Oolite outcrops on the plateau above, but the cliff top itself is a massive slab of hard Lower Calcareous Grit. The cliff is so steep because this hard cap sits on top of softer rocks that get eaten away from underneath the grit. This means that falls of boulders from the higher harder beds are common. The Oxford Clay and Whitby Mudstone are particularly soft.

The other reason for the vertical face is the ice sheet that travelled down the Vale of Mowbray. While this area was probably marked by a steep escarpment on the edge of the upland to the east, the ice sheet ripped its way along, gouging out soft and hard rocks, making a steep slope into a vertical cliff.

Boltby Scar

Just to the north of Sutton Bank is a magnificent exposure of Upper Jurassic rock at Boltby Scar (right). Here the hard layer of Lower Calcareous Grit has been undermined by erosion, leading to a series of huge landslips or 'tumbledowns'. Quarrying has left this vertical face.

Boltby Moor, which is a shelf of rock sticking out at a lower level, is made of the next hard layer down - Long Nab sandstone. It is likely that the ice sheet pushed over this lower layer.

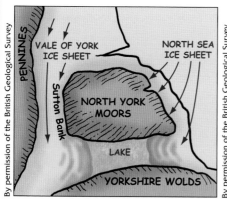

PENNINES

VALE OF YORK ICE SHEET

NORTH SEA ICE SHEET

Sutton Bank

NORTH YORK MOORS

LAKE

YORKSHIRE WOLDS

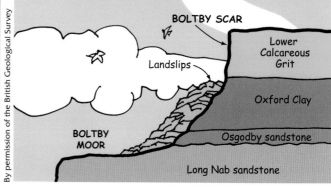

BOLTBY SCAR

Landslips

Lower Calcareous Grit

Oxford Clay

Osgodby sandstone

BOLTBY MOOR

Long Nab sandstone

Whitestone Cliff

A massive slab of Lower Calcareous Grit lies at the top of Sutton Bank. As the softer rock beneath gets eaten away, massive grit boulders tumble down the hillside.

Gormire Lake

One of the few natural lakes in Yorkshire, Gormire is a remnant of the last ice age. As the ice sheet melted boulder clay and water was left behind. The clay has trapped a portion of water and stopped it from draining away.

There are beautiful walks from the National Park Centre on the top of Sutton Bank, including down to Gormire Lake and north to Boltby Scar.

LOWER CALCAREOUS GRIT

This hard yellowish sandstone forms the top layer of the Tabular Hills. It contains some lime, hence the name 'calcareous'. Formed in the Late Jurassic shallow seas the rock is made of tiny grains of silica sand and shell fragments.

Bourgetia

A large marine gastropod, related to snails, which lived on the floor of the shallow Late Jurassic sea.

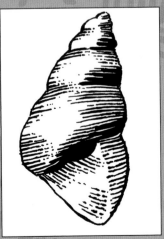

11

Bilsdale and the Hambleton Hills

The western portion of the North York Moors is cut through by the beautiful valley of Bilsdale, running south from the edge of the Cleveland Hills towards Rievaulx. To the west of Bilsdale lies the open moorland of Snilesworth Moor and Hambleton Moor. But a little further south, and entirely different in their geology and landscape, lie the Hambleton Hills. The reason is that the Hambleton Hills are formed from Upper Jurassic rocks laid on top of the Middle Jurassic grits and sandstones of the moors.

The river Seph runs from north to south through Bilsdale (above); the highest land in the National Park (454 metres above sea level) is on Urra Moor just to the east of Bilsdale's northern end. The boulders in the foreground are from the hard sandstone layer of the moorland above Bilsdale.

This idealised section across the western part of the North York Moors (below) shows how Bilsdale and the Hambleton Hills are related. The Upper Jurassic rocks that form the Hambleton Hills are stacked on top of the Middle Jurassic sandstone that forms

Hambleton Moor and the main plateau of the North York Moors. The great conical hills at Coomb, Hawnby and Easterside are outliers from the Hambleton Hills, topped by a layer of Hambleton Oolite.

Bilsdale has been formed by the River Seph; where the Seph flows into the River Rye near Hawnby, the valley then continues as Rye Dale which is a narrower wooded dale cut through the Hambleton Hills.

Dry stone wall repair

The dry stone walls found all over the moors are a good clue to the underlying rock. On the Hambleton Hills, the local oolite breaks into flat slabs that are ideal for walling. Notice the lush green pastures, a sign of the fertile soil fed by the lime content of the underlying Hambleton Oolite.

By permission of the British Geological Survey

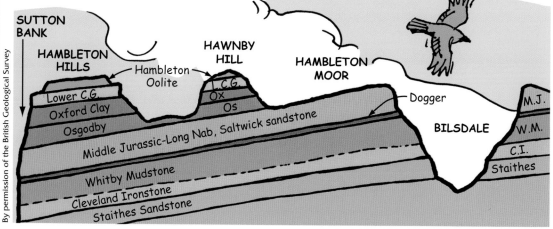

SUTTON BANK

HAMBLETON HILLS

Hambleton Oolite

HAWNBY HILL

HAMBLETON MOOR

Lower C.G.

Oxford Clay

Osgodby

L.C.G.

Ox

Os

Middle Jurassic-Long Nab, Saltwick sandstone

Dogger

M.J.

BILSDALE

W.M.

C.I.

Staithes

Whitby Mudstone

Cleveland Ironstone

Staithes Sandstone

The Hambleton Hills are part of the same geological formation as the Tabular Hills that run along the south side of the moors. This sketch map shows the Upper Jurassic rocks in relation to the older Middle and Lower Jurassic rocks that make up the rest of the North York Moors.

The cap of Easterside Hill (middle, right) is a thin layer of Hambleton Oolite, but the sides of this outlier from the Hambleton Hills are mainly Lower Calcareous Grit, making the soil infertile. The lowest slopes are Oxford Clay which supports pastures.

Bilsdale is formed by the River Seph cutting through the hard cap of Long Nab sandstone down into the soft Whitby Mudstone beneath. The valley cuts further down through the layers of ironstone and sandstone to the Redcar Mudstone in the valley floor.

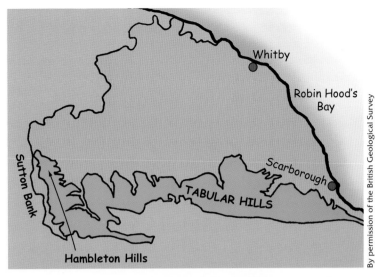

By permission of the British Geological Survey

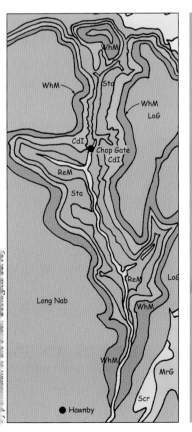

HAMBLETON OOLITE

Hambleton Oolite is the youngest rock found on the moors. Oolites are limestones made up tiny round grain or ooliths. These are formed by microscopic grains of sand or fragments of shells being rolled around on the sea floor, gathering up the sticky limey sediment – a bit like a rolling snowball.

Cardioceras
This beautiful ammonite fossil is found in Upper Jurassic limestones. Ammonites swam freely in the Jurassic seas, using the different chambers in their shells for buoyancy. The shells fell to the sea floor when they died and were preserved as fossils.

13

Kilburn and the Southwest

The southwest margin of the North York Moors has both beautiful landscapes and fascinating geology. Just like at Sutton Bank, the uplands come to a sudden stop at a steep cliff overlooking the area known as the Vale of the White Horse. But the history of this landscape is a little different, as the cliffs have been created by a series of faults. These faults have isolated the Howardian Hills to the south by creating the lowland channel known to geologists as the Coxwold-Gilling Gap.

While it is a magnificent sight, the White Horse of Kilburn is a double pretence. Inspired by the prehistoric white horse at Uffington, Victorian enthusiasts cut horses on chalk hillsides across England. The Kilburn horse, Britain's largest, was cut in 1857. The underlying rock is Upper Calcareous Grit, so chalk is regularly brought to the site to keep the White Horse white.

The Hambleton Hills, Tabular Hills and Howardian Hills (below) are mainly made of Upper Jurassic rocks, while the Wolds to the southeast are made from even younger Chalk. The Coxwold-Gilling Gap links the Vale of York to the Vale of Pickering, a flat lowland vale surrounded by areas of upland.

The Vale of York glacier that pushed south between the North York Moors and the Pennines sent a spur into the gap, blocking off drainage from the Vale of Pickering, which was then a shallow lake.

By permission of the British Geological Survey

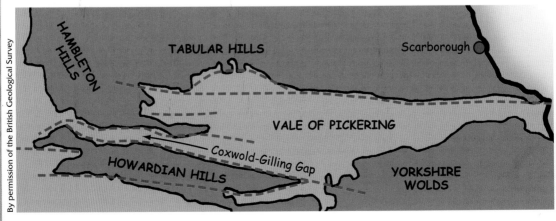

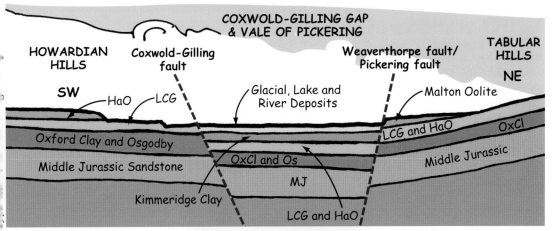

COXWOLD-GILLING GAP & VALE OF PICKERING

HOWARDIAN HILLS — Coxwold-Gilling fault — Weaverthorpe fault/ Pickering fault — TABULAR HILLS

SW — HaO — LCG — Glacial, Lake and River Deposits — Malton Oolite — NE

Oxford Clay and Osgodby — LCG and HaO — OxCl

Middle Jurassic Sandstone — OxCl and Os — Middle Jurassic

MJ

Kimmeridge Clay — LCG and HaO

Coxwold-Gilling Gap

A complex system of geological faults created a channel of low lying land between the Hambleton Hills and the Howardian Hills to the south. The faulting happened mostly in the Tertiary period, long after these Jurassic rocks had been formed and uplifted. The faults generally run from west to east and the land between them has dropped to create a flat valley bottom, now covered in recent mud deposits.

Windy Pits

In this area of the National Park there are several peculiar landscape structures known as Windy Pits (left and below). As streams have cut valleys into the Hambleton Hills, the layer of Calcareous Grit has, in some places, slipped down hill over the underlying Oxford Clay. As the slippage has happened large cracks have appeared between the layers of rock and across the strata.

The fissures in the rock are between 50 cm and 3 metres wide and go down as far as 38 metres below the surface. One set of fissures has been explored and reaches over 300 metres in length. Cracking within the strata leads to fissures opening up on the ground surface. Human remains and artefacts have been found in a number of the Windy Pits; archaeologists believe these were principally left there as ritual offerings. The pits are also home to a variety of bats. The pits are not accessible to the public.

OXFORD CLAY

This soft band of clay was formed in the shallow Late Jurassic seas. Pale grey in colour, the Oxford Clay bed reached thicknesses of over 35 metres. The clay forms the lower slopes of the northern escarpment of the Tabular Hills. Oxford Clay is generally covered in pasture, in contrast to the infertile grit above.

Pleuromya

This bivalve occurs in Upper Jurassic marine strata. It is around 50 mm across. Bivalves are like present-day mussels, attached to the sea floor or rock surfaces, opening and closing their shells to regulate the flow of sea water, while feeding off microscopic nutrients.

Cleveland Hills

The Cleveland Hills form a magnificent arc that marks the boundary between the uplands of the North York Moors and the low-lying Tees Valley. The hard rock (Middle Jurassic sandstone, mudstone and limestone) of the moorland slopes gradually upwards towards the north and west. But this rock is being slowly worn away at its northern edge, forming a steep escarpment. This gives breathtaking views over the Tees Valley. Seen from below the hills are an imposing gateway to the moors.

A view of a section of the Cleveland Hills, looking southwest from Easby Moor. On the flat floodplain below are the villages of Great Broughton and Kirby, with Carlton Bank in the distance.

Alum

Guisborough Forest runs along the northern escarpment of the Cleveland Hills. Its upper levels are marked by the remains of huge alum quarries. The Alum Shale is part of the Whitby Mudstone Formation. The alum industry quarried vast amounts of shale from the Cleveland Hills and the Yorkshire coast from the 1600s until around 1870. The shale was roasted in huge clamps before the alum – used in the textile trade that was the basis of the industrial revolution – was crystallised out of the resulting liquor.

The first alum quarries were at Slapewath and Carlton Bank. The focus of the industry later moved to the coast, where access and transport were easier. Mounds like these in Guisborough forest are made of piles of left-over alum shale.

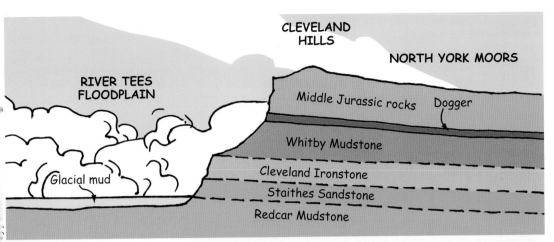

RIVER TEES FLOODPLAIN

CLEVELAND HILLS

NORTH YORK MOORS

Middle Jurassic rocks   Dogger

Whitby Mudstone

Glacial mud

Cleveland Ironstone

Staithes Sandstone

Redcar Mudstone

Middle Jurassic rocks that lie beneath the high moorland of the North York Moors form the flat summits of the Cleveland Hills. The softer mudstones underneath are continually eaten away causing the hard rock to break off giving a steep northward slope. The Whitby Mudstone and Cleveland Ironstone beds have been the source of mineral wealth in this area for centuries.

A Phylloceras ammonite (right) found in loose alum shale left over from the alum quarrying above Hutton Village.

This view of the Cleveland Hills escarpment above Battersby shows a rocky crag at the top. This is an exposure of Long Nab sandstone. The lower slopes are peppered with boulders of sandstone, while further down the Whitby Mudstone supports more fertile soil for pasture.

WHITBY MUDSTONE

Mudstone is an unpromising name for an important rock formation. Within this formation are rock beds known as the Mulgrave Shales, the Alum Shales and the Jet Rock. Each of these has produced valuable minerals.

Huge marine reptiles including plesiosaurs and ichthyosaurs have been found in different beds within the Whitby Mudstone; this is a section of backbone from an ichthyosaur (below) and belemnites (below, left).

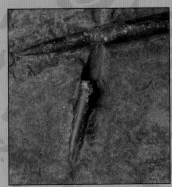

Roseberry Topping

This remarkable hill is the best-known landmark in the lower Tees Valley. A hard slab of sandstone sits on top of Roseberry Topping, while the soft Whitby Mudstone is eaten away from beneath. The hill also owes its shape to mining – ironstone on the lower slopes was dug out in the past, leading to the collapse of one side of the hill. The climb to the top gives spectacular views over Teesside and along the Cleveland Hills.

Roseberry Topping is an outlier of the Cleveland Hills. The hard layer that sits on top of the hills is being slowly eroded from the northern and western edge of the hills. The small piece on Roseberry Topping is a remnant of that erosion that will eventually disappear.

Because the rock strata tilt upwards towards the north, the northern edge is being continually worn away.

Geology is a continuous process - the material worn off these hills is eventually washed into rivers and seas, where it is laid down to form future rocks.

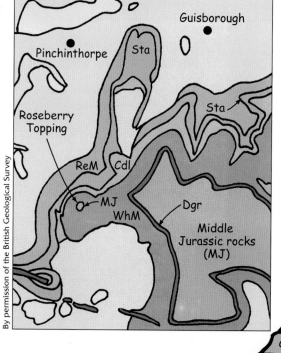

By permission of the British Geological Survey

By permission of the British Geological Survey

Wainstones

The Wainstones are on the sharp edge of the Cleveland Hills, facing north over the Tees Valley. Erosion has exposed the thick slab of Middle Jurassic sandstone that forms the cap of the hills. As rain and wind wears away the soft rock underneath, huge square boulders break off. You can see these boulders strewn around the lower slopes of the hills.

The west face of Roseberry Topping (below) is a massive cliff of yellow moorland sandstone, in this case from the Saltwick formation. Notice the huge boulders of sandstone that have broken away from the cliff face and tumbled down the slope.

Eston Hills

The Eston Hills comprise another outlier of the Cleveland Hills. They are separated by a wide flat valley in which the town of Guisborough sits. The valley is a small rift valley or graben – the central section has slipped down the faults on either side; the valley floor is covered in glacial deposits.

CLEVELAND IRONSTONE

The sandstone and ironstone formation, reddish in colour and hard, contains a number of seams that are rich in high-grade iron ore. The Main Seam is up to 4 metres thick.

Pseudopecten

A large marine bivalve found in Lower Jurassic rocks, particularly the Cleveland Ironstone. The Pecten Seam is one of the principal iron ore seams in Cleveland.

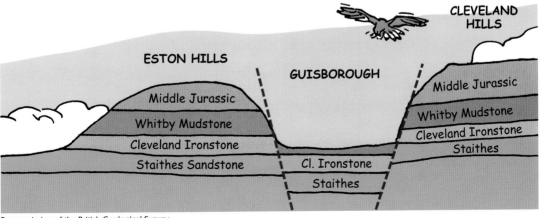

By permission of the British Geological Survey

Upper Eskdale

The River Esk begins its 50-kilometre journey to the sea in Westerdale, before flowing into the broad open expanse of upper Eskdale. The beautiful landscape of upper Eskdale has one peculiarity which comes from its recent geological history. We might expect an upland stream to create a narrow valley, and then gradually open out into a broad floodplain. But the Esk does the opposite – upper Eskdale is broad and quite flat, while lower Eskdale is steep and narrow. The cause of this upside-down dale can be found in the last ice age.

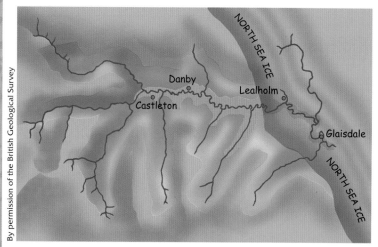

By permission of the British Geological Survey

Ice sheets pushed in from the North Sea and down the Vale of York but were not thick enough to cover the high ground of the North York Moors. One piece of the North Sea ice pushed up into Eskdale, probably as far as Lealholm. This wall of ice blocked all the drainage from the moors to the sea and created a glacial lake. A layer of mud was deposited on the floor of the lake giving upper Eskdale its level appearance. A bank of glacial mud known as a moraine also marks the furthest extent of the ice sheet near Lealholm.

Commondale is now a quiet hamlet in upper Eskdale but until 60 years ago it was the site of a major industrial works, containing brickworks, pottery and pipe-making. Commondale pottery is highly prized: the works closed in 1947.

Like the other dales that cut through the central part of the moors Eskdale is capped on either side by Middle Jurassic moorland sandstone (see section below). The Dogger marks the boundary between this and the Lower Jurassic rocks beneath.

As well as supporting pasture fields, the Whitby Mudstone Formation contains alum and cement shales as well as jet rock, with the Cleveland Ironstone formation lying just beneath. These, together with the whinstone from the Cleveland Dyke and local clay for brick and pottery works, made the Esk valley a centre for industry until the mid twentieth century.

The Esk rises at the top of Westerdale. The width of these dales shows their age – they were in existence before the last ice age when they were probably filled by the waters of a glacial lake. The heather moorland is on Middle Jurassic sandstone, while the pastures of the dalesides are on Lower Jurassic mudstones and ironstones.

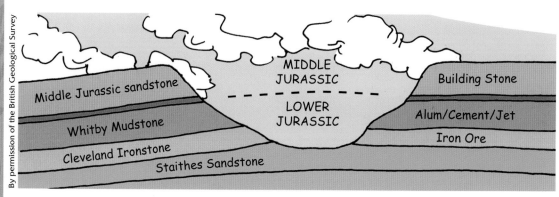

By permission of the British Geological Survey

DOGGER

From Castleton station to beyond Houlsyke the River Esk meanders gently through a flat open plain. The meanders, like this one near Danby (above), are cut through the old lake deposits from the last ice age, by a river flowing on a fairly level course.

The Dogger bed is an important marker bed for geologists. Made of hard, brittle, reddish sandstone and ironstone it tends to stand out when the softer rocks around it have been worn away, and it marks the boundary between the Lower and Middle Jurassic periods. The term dogger is often used for hard rocks or rocks with hard nodules.

Trigonia
Trigonia is a marine bivalve found in rocks of the later Lower Jurassic period. Its characteristic shape is like a three-sided pyramid.

Upper Eskdale is a broad open expanse (left). A dale that was already here was filled with water for several thousand years during the last ice age, with a broad thick layer of mud being deposited at the bottom. A succession of ice ages saw a variety of large mammals, including mammoths, inhabiting this region.

Lower Eskdale

The lower part of Eskdale is a beautiful and surprising landscape. From Glaisdale to Whitby the Esk has cut a series of steep sided gorges, behaving like a youthful mountain stream. But in its upper reaches around Danby and Lealholm the river winds gently through an open flat-bottomed valley. The reason for this upside down valley lies in its geological history. Lower Eskdale is actually a new river valley cut since the last ice age; while we expect a river to have a wide floodplain as it nears the coast, the deep gorge of the Esk runs all the way to Whitby.

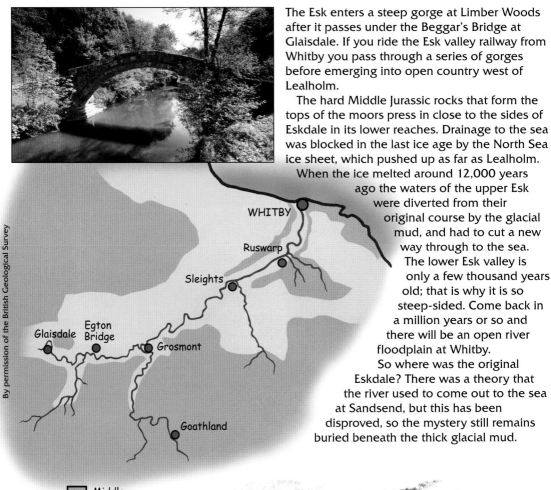

The Esk enters a steep gorge at Limber Woods after it passes under the Beggar's Bridge at Glaisdale. If you ride the Esk valley railway from Whitby you pass through a series of gorges before emerging into open country west of Lealholm.

The hard Middle Jurassic rocks that form the tops of the moors press in close to the sides of Eskdale in its lower reaches. Drainage to the sea was blocked in the last ice age by the North Sea ice sheet, which pushed up as far as Lealholm. When the ice melted around 12,000 years ago the waters of the upper Esk were diverted from their original course by the glacial mud, and had to cut a new way through to the sea. The lower Esk valley is only a few thousand years old; that is why it is so steep-sided. Come back in a million years or so and there will be an open river floodplain at Whitby.

So where was the original Eskdale? There was a theory that the river used to come out to the sea at Sandsend, but this has been disproved, so the mystery still remains buried beneath the thick glacial mud.

By permission of the British Geological Survey

WHITBY
Ruswarp
Sleights
Glaisdale Egton Bridge Grosmont
Goathland

☐ Middle Jurassic rocks
☐ Glacial Till and River Deposits

The lower Esk valley was an industrial hub through most of the nineteenth century. Ironstone was processed at Glaisdale and Grosmont before being taken by rail and ship to Teesside and further afield.

By the time it reaches Sleights the Esk has cut a deep gorge. The road bridge is high above the river, and the north face of Eskdale is a steep wooded slope.

STAITHES SANDSTONE

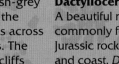

This is a slightly reddish-grey sandstone that forms the lower part of the dales across the North York Moors. The lower part of the sea cliffs and the scar at Staithes are formed from this sandstone.

Dactylioceras
A beautiful ribbed ammonite commonly found in the Lower Jurassic rocks of the moors and coast. *Dactylioceras* specimens measure around 50mm across

This barn at the dale head of Glaisdale shows the steepness of the dale side. The barn is made of square cut blocks of Middle Jurassic sandstone from the moors above.

The North Sea ice sheet pushed inland as far as Glaisdale. The flat bottom of the valley is made of glacial till.

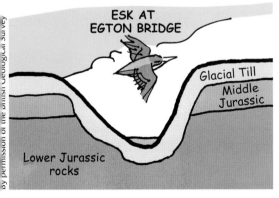

By permission of the British Geological Survey

At Egton Bridge the floor of Eskdale is covered in a layer of glacial till, showing that there was a valley here before the ice age. The Esk has made this deeper and steeper. Near Whitby the river seems to

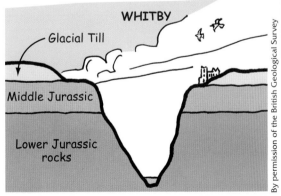

By permission of the British Geological Survey

be in a completely new valley; it has stripped away the glacial till from the ground surface, and cut through the hard Middle Jurassic rock to scour a deep gorge.

23

The Northern Dales

A series of spectacular and beautiful dales run from the high moorland down into Eskdale. Kildale and Commondale run southwards. Baysdale, Westerdale (which carries the Esk from its source), Danby Dale, Fryup Dale and Glaisdale run northwards, followed to the west by the dale of the Murk Esk and Iburndale. Each of these dales has been formed by a small stream cutting through the hard layer of Middle Jurassic rocks lying on top of the high plateau of the moors. Softer, more fertile Lower Jurassic rocks are exposed along the sides and floors of the dales, leading to a picturesque contrast between the moor tops and the rich green pastures of the dales.

This spectacular view of Danby Dale (above) shows off many of its geological features. Just visible in the foreground is a crag of hard blocky moorland sandstone. These crags are often found along the upper rims of the dales. On the far side the moorland pushes down from the tops, about a quarter of the way down the dale. This shows the break between the moorland sandstone and the softer more fertile mudstone that lies beneath. Under the flat floor of the dale lies a shelf of hard Staithes Sandstone, with the beck occasionally cutting through to the Redcar Mudstone beneath.

Great Fryup Dale (below) has glacial deposits which make it flatter than other dales.

Fryupdale

The double dale of Fryup is separated into two by an outlier of hard Long Nab gritstone laying on top of the softer Whitby Mudstone. This forms a high piece of ground called the Heads.

The ice sheet that pushed up

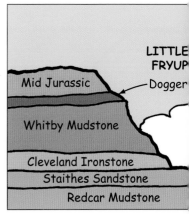

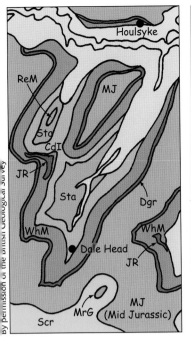

By permission of the British Geological Survey

REDCAR MUDSTONE

This is a 250 metre thick layer of shale that lies at the base of the Jurassic rocks of north east Yorkshire. The grey shales form the bottoms of many of the dales in the region and are at the foot of the cliffs on the northern part of the coast. Redcar Mudstone contains iron and is rich in marine fossils.

Pentacrinites

The crinoid family is one of the most physically diverse in the fossil record. Based on five divisions, they include the sea anemones and sea lilies as well as starfish. *Pentacrinites* is a sea lily. Pieces of stem are quite commonly found and easily recognised by their five-sided structure.

the Esk valley came into Great Fryup and left behind a layer of glacial till. It did not reach up as far as Little Fryup Dale, which has bedrock beneath its covering of soil.

The dales are divided into pasture fields by stone walls and hedges, with the pasture used for cattle, sheep and winter fodder.

Walls are used as field boundaries, marking the border between moorland and pasture, following the geological divide between the sandstone of the moorland and the mudstone of the dalesides. In the eighteenth century there were attempts to cultivate parts of the moorland by ploughing in huge amounts of lime, but this came to nothing.

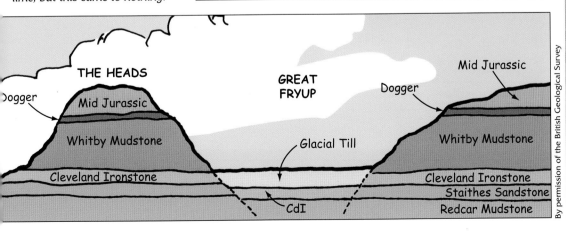

THE HEADS

GREAT FRYUP

Mid Jurassic

Dogger

Dogger

Mid Jurassic

Whitby Mudstone

Glacial Till

Whitby Mudstone

Cleveland Ironstone

Cleveland Ironstone

Staithes Sandstone

CdI

Redcar Mudstone

By permission of the British Geological Survey

Cliffs and coves

The cliffs of the North Yorkshire coast are made of layers of Jurassic rock towering above the North Sea. From Hunt Cliff at Saltburn in the north to Filey Brigg in the south, an almost unbroken succession of cliffs is interrupted only by small coves and the occasional sandy beach.

The cliffs are so high and steep because the same hard rocks that form the plateaux of the high moors and the Tabular Hills also make the tops of the cliffs. Inland the hard cap has been worn through by wind, rain and streams cutting down from above; on the coast the sea eats away at the softer rocks from beneath, causing boulders to break off from the hard, brittle sandstones above.

At Whitby's East Cliff the hard cap of sandstone is at the top. Part of the Middle Jurassic formation is made up of dark shales formed in the stagnant marsh of a delta. In the foreground is the hard band of Dogger, lying between the Middle Jurassic and the Lower Jurassic.

The cliffs at Cloughton, in the southern part of the coast show how the rock layers dip gradually towards the south. The top layer is hard sandstone, then the softer Scarborough Limestone, then Cloughton sandstone forming the lower shelf of the cliff.

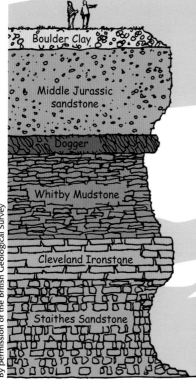

Boulder Clay

Middle Jurassic sandstone

Dogger

Whitby Mudstone

Cleveland Ironstone

Staithes Sandstone

Wave-cut platform or scar

Sea level

By permission of the British Geological Survey

This section of cliff is from the north of the Yorkshire coast. The hard layer of sandstone is resistant to erosion, but the soft layers beneath are being eaten away by the sea. The result is that huge lumps of sandstone break off and tumble down. This combination of hard cap and soft underbelly is what makes the cliffs high and steep.

Above the sandstone is a layer of boulder clay. This is a relic of the last ice age, left behind when the ice sheets melted around 11,500 years ago.

The picturesque towns and villages on the Heritage Coast are all built into gullies cut into the hard sandstone by streams, which then slice through the soft shales to form steep-sided valleys.

In the cliffs around Staithes and Port Mulgrave the hard bands of Cleveland Ironstone stand out. The Dogger is a thin band of hard rock that lies beneath the Middle Jurassic sandstone and marks the boundary between the Lower and Middle Jurassic.

Where a layer of soft rock lies at sea level, as at Sandsend and Scarborough, sandy beaches are formed. More commonly on the Heritage Coast, a layer of harder rock lies at sea level and it forms a wave-cut platform, or scar.

Jet is a fossilised wood that occurs in a particular bed within the Whitby Mudstone Formation. Jet is made out of the fossilised trunks of monkey-puzzle trees that grew along the coast, and were washed into the sea when they fell. The wood of the trees was fossilised and preserved in the shales forming at the bottom of the Jurassic sea. When cut and polished, jet attains a beautiful deep lustrous black colour; Whitby jet is prized all over the world.

At Deepgrove Wyke (above), north of Sandsend, Middle Jurassic sandstone forms the top layer of the cliff, with the Dogger bed visible about a quarter of the way down. Below this is the Whitby Mudstone. The upper part of the Whitby Mudstone is soft Alum Shales, while the bottom section here is harder Mulgrave Shales, which contain Jet Rock. The holes in the foot of the cliff have been dug by miners in search of jet.

At Robin Hood's Bay (right) the long arch of rocks that forms the central plateau of the North York Moors reaches the sea. Here another geological feature forms the arc of the bay. In the Tertiary period forces from different directions pushed against the rock strata and made them buckle upwards into a dome. The dome is curved on all sides and lends its shape to the bay.

The sea has worn away a wave-cut platform that reveals the underlying rock structure at Robin Hood's Bay – seen here from Ravenscar. If you measure the slope of the beds on the scar, and sketch their continuation upwards, you can see the shape of the dome.

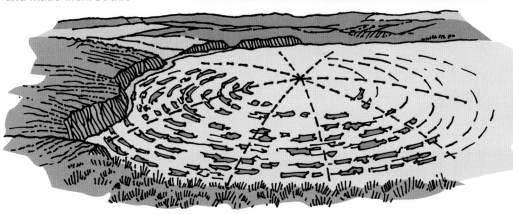

Coastal plain

Between the high cliffs of the coast and the heather moorland lies a captivating strip of undulating green pasture land. The pasture fields lie on top of glacial till deposits left behind by the North Sea ice sheet when it melted around 11,500 years ago. The ice sheet pushed in as far as the high ground of the North York Moors, suggesting that there was already some kind of coastal plateau. The glacial clay has produced soil that is fertile enough for rich pastureland and some arable farming.

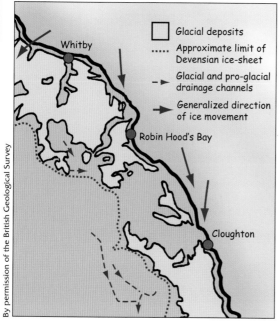

Glacial deposits

····· Approximate limit of Devensian ice-sheet

Glacial and pro-glacial drainage channels

Generalized direction of ice movement

Whitby

Robin Hood's Bay

Cloughton

This view at Boulby (above, left) shows heather moorland in the foreground, on the highest ground which the ice sheets did not cover, and the lower-lying plateau of pasture and arable land on the glacial till in the distance.

The cliff tops are made from a thick layer of hard moorland sandstone, so we would expect heather moorland to reach right to the edge of the cliff. But a layer of glacial till lies on top of the sandstone, giving a wide strip of fertile ground for farming, as here just east of Staithes (above).

The North Sea ice sheet pushed inland but did not penetrate the higher ground of the moors. The coastal plateau was mostly covered in ice from the Tees Valley south to Robin Hood's Bay and from Cloughton southwards, though high ground around Boulby and Ravenscar kept these areas clear of glacial till.

This sketch section shows glacial till covering the plain between the high moorland and the cliffs.

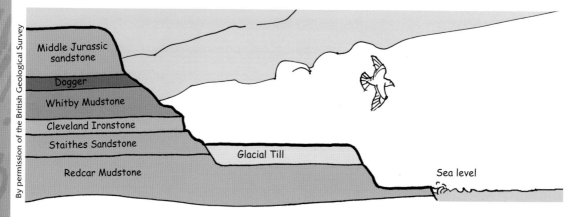

Middle Jurassic sandstone

Dogger

Whitby Mudstone

Cleveland Ironstone

Staithes Sandstone

Redcar Mudstone

Glacial Till

Sea level

This view from near Ravenscar (above) shows Brow Moor in the foreground, where a layer of sandstone lies near to the surface. Lower down in the great stepped bowl of Robin Hood's Bay, ice sheets pushed in. The resulting glacial till forms the low cliffs around the bay. There are similar glacial clay cliffs at Sandsend.

Boulders carried along and dumped by the ice sheets are known as erratics. These help us to plot the range and direction of travel of the ice. There is no granite bedrock in this area. This erratic (above, right) at Crossgates near Scarborough is made of a distinctive granite (right) from Shap Fell in the Lake District.

GLACIAL TILL

Glacial till is used to describe deposits of mud, clay and boulders left behind when ice sheets melt. The make-up of the till varies, though mostly it is boulder clay, formed by fragments of rock being dragged along beneath the ice sheet and then dumped in a casing of clay-rich mud.

Mammoth tooth
Remains of the animals that inhabited the region during the ice ages show that the environment was tundra. Mammals like reindeer, wolverine, fox, bear and hare were here, along with mammoth and woolly rhinoceros. This mammoth tooth was found at the coast near Flamborough Head, just south of our area. Ice age remains have not had time to become fossilised, instead the bones are preserved in mud.

The pebbles on Yorkshire's beaches owe their huge variety to the ice sheets. A whole range of rocks were brought to the region from the north by ice. These large pebbles at Cloughton Wyke have been rounded off by the continuous action of the sea.

29

High Moors

The central feature of the North York Moors is the unbroken expanse of heather moorland that lies at its heart. The moorland has been created by a combination of natural environment and human activity dating back as far as the Bronze Age. In that time the landscape has changed from mixed woodland to a combination of peat bogs and heather moor; and all the time the main influence has been the underlying rocks. The rock beneath the high moorland is a thick layer of gritty sandstone formed in the Middle Jurassic period. On these pages we are going to look in a little more detail at those moorland rocks.

The heather moorlands are a human creation. In the warming that followed the end of the last ice age around 11,500 years ago the moors became covered in a mixed forest, firstly 'pioneer' species such as birch, willow and hazel, then later by oak, lime and alder. Humans came to the area during the Mesolithic era, from 10,000 to 6,000 years ago and began burning and felling trees and undergrowth as part of a hunting strategy.

By 3,500 years ago the tree cover had mostly gone; soil nutrients leached out leaving a heathland vegetation.

Layers of peat accumulate most readily in wet acid conditions. Dead vegetation is preserved in layers, slowly building up great thicknesses. Peat bogs can be as much as 10 metres deep.

In some places heather grows directly on peat, in others a thin band of soil lies between sandstone and

heather (below, left).

In the last couple of centuries humans have intervened again and the heather moorland has been preserved as an ideal habitat for game birds. Each section is regularly burned off under controlled conditions.

At Eller Beck (below) great slabs of sandstone have been broken away and transported by the action of glacial meltwater and more recent floods.

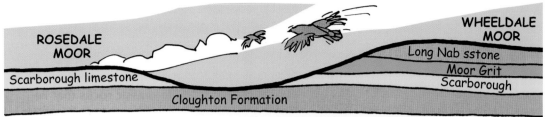

ROSEDALE MOOR

Scarborough limestone

Cloughton Formation

WHEELDALE MOOR

Long Nab sstone

Moor Grit

Scarborough

By permission of the British Geological Survey

All the rocks on the high moors are of Middle Jurassic age, formed when this region was a river delta on the coast of a subtropical sea. The lowest set of rocks here is the Cloughton Formation, a fine sandstone formed in the freshwater channels of the delta. This formation contains lots of plant fossils. Above that comes the Scarborough limestone, a set of marine rocks that shows that sea levels rose and flooded the area. Above the Scarborough limestone comes the Moor Grit, a hard gritstone, and then above that the Long Nab Member, of mudstone and sandstone.

The geology of the Middle Jurassic is a bit more complicated because of the environment. Deltas and coasts are always active, changing landscapes, with lots of different environments within them, and rocks being laid down and worn away at the same time. Unlike the marine rocks, the non-marine beds of the Middle Jurassic do not always stretch for great

LONG NAB

The Long Nab Member of the Middle Jurassic rocks makes up a large part of the hard cap of the moorland. A mix of river siltstone and sandstone, this was formed in the coastal delta that dominated this region.

Thick, hard and flat-lying, the Long Nab grit member forms much of the central plateau.

Dinosaur footprint

In the Middle Jurassic period dinosaurs roamed along the coast, with its rich vegetation. No dinosaur bones have been found here, suggesting that conditions for fossilisation were not good. But dinosaur footprints are relatively plentiful, giving information about height, weight, claws and agility.

distances, and the material in those rocks is often being re-worked. To see this in action just visit a beach where the tide is continually bringing in layers of sand and then

washing them out again. This geological map of Wheeldale and Glaisdale Moor shows different layers of Middle Jurassic rock underlying the moors at different places.

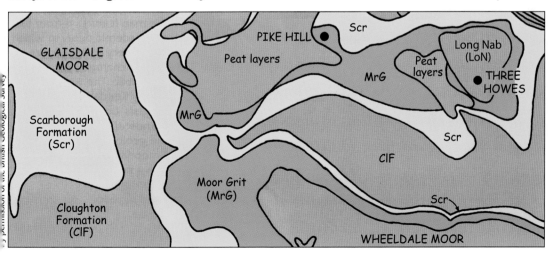

By permission of the British Geological Survey

GLAISDALE MOOR

PIKE HILL

Scr

Peat layers

MrG

Peat layers

Long Nab (LoN)

THREE HOWES

Scarborough Formation (Scr)

MrG

Scr

ClF

Moor Grit (MrG)

Cloughton Formation (ClF)

Scr

WHEELDALE MOOR

31

Slacks and Swangs on the High Moorland

The high moorland owes its present appearance to the Middle Jurassic rocks that lie beneath and to human intervention – felling trees and burning off heather to preserve the vegetation. But the moorland is not a uniform landscape, and the variations in topography and vegetation give us more clues to its fascinating history.

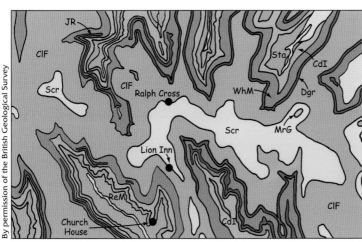

By permission of the British Geological Survey

Ice sheets are complex environments, dynamic and powerful with huge forces working on the landscape. Although frozen water makes up the bulk of the ice sheet, there are channels of running water beneath and around the ice, and when the ice melts vast amounts of water are released.

The moorland to the north and south of Eskdale has a number of channels carved by glacial meltwater, and these make spectacular landforms. They are quite distinct because they look like valleys carved by great rivers, but the rivers are no longer there, or are reduced to small becks. The local names for these valleys are slacks or swangs – look carefully on an Ordnance Survey map and you will see them dotted all across the moorland.

This is Bella Dale Slack near Scaling Dam (top), a typical moorland slack. The drainage channel cut by meltwater is now filled by a bog.

The map (centre) is from the 1909 academic paper in which the discovery of the ice age lakes and channels was first made public. The work, by Percy Fry Kendall, changed geologists' understanding of the landscape of the moors.

The geological map (left) of the moorland above Rosedale shows a swathe of Scarborough Limestone, marked in yellow. See the box opposite.

The dry stone walls of the moors and dales are made from square blocks of moorland sandstone. Contrast the shape of these with the flat stones of walls and houses in the Hambleton and Tabular Hills.

In the Middle Jurassic Period this region was covered by a large river delta, draining land to the west and north. Conifers, gingkos and tree ferns grew in profusion, and dinosaurs left their footprints in the mud and sandbanks of the delta.

SCARBOROUGH LIMESTONE

The Middle Jurassic Period saw sea levels fall and the region changed from sea to a feshwater delta. But within this span of 20 or so million years there were periods when sea levels rose and the region was submerged. In one of these intervals a bed of limestone was laid down on the shallow sea floor, and this is known as the Scarborough Limestone Formation. The grey limestone is best seen on the scar in Scarborough's South Bay, but it also lies directly beneath a large section of the high moorland above Rosedale Head.

Astarte

Astarte is a fairly common but distinctive bivalve. The presence of marine fossils in a limestone formation shows the rise in sea levels in one interval of the generally land-dominated Middle Jurassic environment.

Cleveland Dyke

Great landmark of the region, the Cleveland Dyke runs arrow straight across the northern part of the North York Moors. This is the only igneous rock formation in northeast Yorkshire; it forms a straight ridge, known locally as the Whinstone Ridge, running roughly from Blea Hill on the Fylingdales Moor in the east, across Eskdale and to the north. This is where the dyke reaches the surface; beneath ground it reaches out into the North Sea and up to the western isles of Scotland, forming part of a swarm of dykes. The Cleveland Dyke near Goathland is now an amazing sight as the hard rock has been quarried out, leaving a trough up to 20 metres deep.

The Cleveland Dyke near Goathland was originally a ridge caused by a hot slice of magma pushing up to the surface of the earth. While the sides of the ridge are still visible, the dyke is now a gigantic quarried trough, stretching across the high moors and Eskdale. Along the sides of the trough that marks the Cleveland Dyke there are signs of the local Jurassic rock being baked by the sudden injection of hot magma.

This section (left) shows layers of rock deep beneath the surface. The Cleveland Dyke slices through these older rocks before reaching the surface on the North York Moors.

The straight line of the Cleveland Dyke, marked in red on the map (below), crosses the boundaries between the other rocks, showing that it is a younger formation. The dyke was formed when a massive igneous event beneath western Scotland pushed hot magma outwards around 58 million years ago. Some of the magma found its way up through weaknesses in the earth's upper crust.

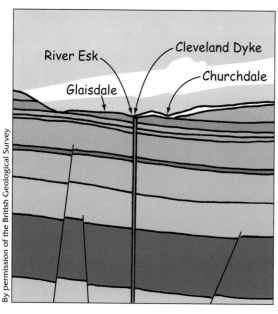

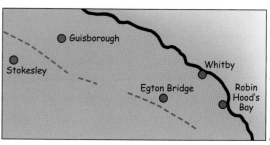

The Cleveland Dyke is the most southerly of a swarm of dykes created by underground igneous activity around 58 million years ago. A significant eruption was centred roughly beneath the Isle of Mull, around 350 kilometres away, though it may be that the Cleveland Dyke was pushed out of a reservoir of hot magma beneath the southern uplands of Scotland. Related dykes outcrop on the surface across southwest Scotland and on the coast of Northumberland. The Cleveland Dyke reaches the surface south of Carlisle and in the upper Tees Valley before reaching the North York Moors.

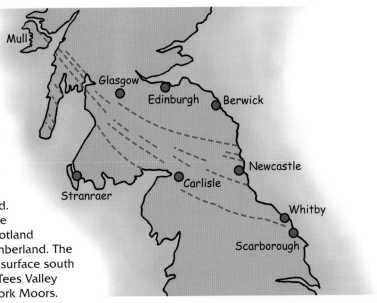

By permission of the British Geological Survey

The rock from the Cleveland Dyke was known locally as whinstone - a term used by stone merchants for dark rock. The extremely hard stone was dug out and broken into regular pieces for use as setts or cobbles. Tramways were built across the moors to take the stone down to the railway at Grosmont, from where it was taken to pave the streets of Middlesbrough and Leeds.

These photos show the effects of the hot magma on the surrounding sandstones and shales.

CLEVELAND DYKE

The rock of the Cleveland Dyke is a dolerite, a dark and fine-grained igneous rock type. The sedimentary rocks that dominate this region have been laid down in seas or deltas. The sandstones and mudstones are recycled rocks - sand and silt being worn away from existing rocks by seas and rivers. But the Cleveland Dyke dolerite is made from magma superheated and pressurised before being injected up into the earth's crust.

The fine grain of the dolerite (compared with, for example, granite) shows that the dyke cooled very quickly, as we would expect in such a narrow fissure. The photos above show how the surrounding sedimentary rocks were baked by the injection of hot magma.

Newtondale

One of the most spectacular landscape features of the region, Newtondale cuts a deep and winding gorge through the southern part of the moors. It is a stunning example of a glacial outflow channel – a waterway carved by the run-off from ice age lakes and ice sheets. The keys to Newtondale's history are its narrowness and depth, which show that it is a recent landform, and the way that the valley winds with the stream, which shows that it was carved very rapidly.

Though rivers often take a winding course, their valleys are generally straightened out over time. Newtondale gorge itself winds in a series of open meanders. This shows that the gorge was formed rapidly by the sudden outflow of a large amount of water, cutting its way down through the plateau of the moors. The waters came from the drainage trapped in upper Eskdale. During and after the last ice age there were vast quantities of water trapped in ice sheets and glacial lakes – and all this water had to go somewhere.

The meltwater overflowing from Lake Eskdale and the North Sea ice sheet cut a channel through the thick layer of moorland grit. Just west of the Hole of Horcum the gorge begins to cut through the Tabular Hills. At Yew Tree Scar, on the edge of Levisham Moor (left), a hard layer of Osgodby Formation sandstone is exposed as a spectacular crag overlooking Newtondale gorge.

CORNBRASH

A relatively thin layer of the rock known as Cornbrash sits at the top of the Middle Jurassic sediments. Cornbrash was named by the geological pioneer William Smith after the loose rubble, or brash, on which corn was grown in Wiltshire and Oxfordshire. Smith worked in that region before ending his days in Scarborough. In Yorkshire the Cornbrash is a dark grey limestone and sandstone mix, full of fragments of shells, showing the change to a shallow sea. Its coarse grains and purple-grey colour make it quite distinct.

Avicula

Avicula echinata is a small bivalve, around 1 cm across. Fragments of its shells are commonly found in Cornbrash sediments.

The gorge was used by George Stephenson for part of the route of the Whitby to Pickering railway in 1836. Newtondale now carries the North Yorkshire Moors Railway, which runs steam and diesel trains between Pickering and Grosmont, and on to Whitby.

Newtondale provides a link between Eskdale and the Vale of Pickering. The gorge was formed as an outflow channel from the ice age Lake Eskdale. The gorge grows shallower as the land slopes down towards the south, with the waters emerging at Newbridge. Pickering sits on top of the debris washed out of the gorge.

—————— Lake shoreline

- - - - - - - Outflow channel

▬▬▬▬ Ice front

Guisborough
Lake Eskdale   Whitby
NORTH SEA
Newtondale   Hackness
Gorge   Lake   Scarborough
Helmsley   Forge Valley
Pickering
Lake Pickering   Filey
Malton

By permission of the British Geological Survey

Fen Bog

The stream that runs through Newtondale rises at Fen Bog. Here the peat reaches over 12 metres in depth. When the Pickering to Whitby railway was built in the 1830s sheep's wool was tipped into the bog (above) to help give a firm platform. Fen Bog is a Nature Reserve which supports a huge variety of plants, insects, birds and reptiles. After the last ice age the waters of the Esk flowed eastwards to the sea and Newtondale lost its supply of water.

Rosedale Ironstone

The high moorland is in the form of an arch running from west to east. A series of magnificent dales runs down either side of this arch. To the north the dales run into Eskdale and to the south they run as far as the Tabular Hills, where they are dramatically altered by the change in geology. The southern moorland dales include Bransdale, Farndale and Rosedale. Here we look in detail at Rosedale – now a peaceful dale but once, due to its geology, a hive of industry.

Like the other moorland dales, Rosedale has been cut through the hard crust of moorland grit into the soft Lower Jurassic rocks beneath. Those rocks include a thick layers of Dogger and Cleveland Ironstone, and for several hundred years Rosedale had a thriving ironstone industry. The ironstone was mined in the lower part of the dale, near to the village of Rosedale Abbey, and then transported on railways along either side of the valley. The routes of the railways are still highly visible.

The iron ore was tipped into kilns on both sides of the dale, for calcining. This process reduced the impurities in the ore and its weight. The calcined ore was tipped into iron wagons and taken across the moors.

Bell Top forms a kind of inland headland in the middle of Rosedale. Seen here from the east it projects out into the dale. The boundary between the moorland grit and the Lower Jurassic rocks is clearly marked in the change in vegetation from forest and heather moorland to pasture fields.

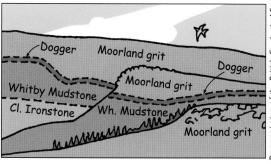

The Cleveland Ironstone outcrops in the lower part of the dale with the Dogger ironstone higher up. Mining was by drift mines sunk into the side of the dale and occasional vertical shafts meeting the seams from above. Some drifts reached as far as 500 metres into the ironstone.

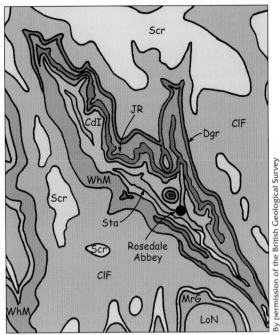

By permission of the British Geological Survey

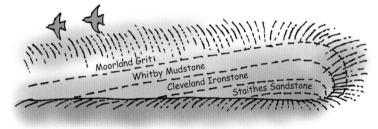

Railways ran up either side of Rosedale and then across the high part of the moorland to near Ingleby. Here the railway met the western escarpment of the moors and went down a steep incline towards Battersby junction.

This 1925 photograph (top) shows the effects of the ironstone mining on the east side of Rosedale. The railway lines are clearly visible.

This 1900 photograph (above) shows the incline that took the Rosedale railway over the escarpment near Ingleby. At the top was a drum house with a huge winch used to wind the wagons to the top.

The map of the surface geology (above, right) makes Rosedale seem like a complete bowl, with the Lower Jurassic layers beneath the green layer of moorland grit.

In reality, the ring of strata is caused by the different dips of the land surface and the rock beds. The land slopes to the south, but the strata slope at a slightly steeper rate, so that the Lower Jurassic rocks disappear beneath the land surface at the southern end.

OSGODBY

The Osgodby Formation was deposited during the Middle Jurassic period, as sea levels were beginning to rise before the long-term submerging of the area in the Upper Jurassic. It is a sandstone formation formed in coastal waters. It supports a more fertile soil than the moorland grits; the pastureland below Saltergate Brow extending out into the moors, for example, is underlain by Osgodby Sandstone.

Ornithella
This is a small marine brachiopod. The hole in the larger shell where the stalk or pedicle was used to anchor the animal to rocks is clearly visible on most fossils.

39

The Tabular Hills

The Tabular Hills run from west to east along the southern part of the National Park, all the way from Bilsdale to the coast at Scarborough. The underlying geology of these hills produces a beautifully varied landscape including dry valleys, wooded dales, open pasture land, forests and, on the northern margin, a spectacular escarpment.

The Tabular Hills are made from rocks of Upper Jurassic age, which sit on top of the Middle Jurassic rocks that form the great plateau of the central moorland. These Upper Jurassic rocks are a mixture of limestones and lime-rich, or calcareous, sandstones. The high limestone content makes them quite different from the rocks of the central moorland. The lime-rich soil supports a range of wild plants that flourish on the verges and pathways of this landscape. Wild flowers include rock rose, viper's bugloss, marjoram and orchids. They also allow farmers to grow pasture and arable crops. The limestone is also much more porous, soaking up water, creating dry valleys (below, left) and underground streams.

The characteristic profile of the northern escarpment is seen all the way from Scarborough to Helmsley. Woodland marks the Lower Calcareous Grit, with pastures on the gently sloping Oxford Clay and Osgodby Formation sandstone.

Travelling from south to north you cross the magnificent escarpment that marks the northern edge of the Tabular Hills (map below). To the south, the hills slope gently down to the Vale of Pickering. These different slopes are dictated by the dip of the underlying rock strata.

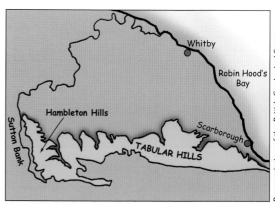

By permission of the British Geological Survey

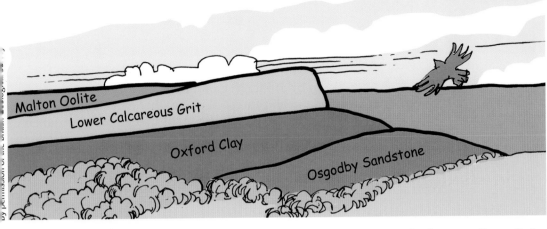

Malton Oolite
Lower Calcareous Grit
Oxford Clay
Osgodby Sandstone

The rock beds of the Tabular hills all dip down to the south. The steep escarpment is formed because a hard cap of grit sits on top of softer mudstone (clay). The rock types are reflected in the plant cover. Limestones such as Malton Oolite provide good agricultural soils. The calcareous grit is suitable for trees, particularly on its steep side. The forests at Broxa, Dalby and Cropton are planted over calcareous grit. Below this the clays give gentler slopes and are more suitable for pasture. The lime-rich rocks soak up water which causes problems for villages on the tops of the hills. These 'dry' villages used to channel water from the high moors, while farmers built clay-lined ponds to conserve water.

This spectacular rock face below Gillamoor (above) is on the northern escarpment of the Tabular Hills. It shows a layer of white limestone sitting on top of yellow calcareous grit or sandstone. The lower slopes, formed from Oxford Clay, are covered in brush and bracken.

The Tabular Hills are noted for their limestone flora, including cowslips and orchids.

CORALLINE OOLITE

The Upper Jurassic rocks of the Tabular Hills were formed in a warm, shallow sea. Limestones were formed at the bottom of the sea, but also through the action of reef-building corals. The limestones are sometimes known as the Coralline Oolite Formation because of the corals and reefs preserved in the rocks. The photo shows a mass of bivalve shells in Coralline rock.

Iastraea
This compound coral is *Iastraea explanata*. Like other shell fish, corals use the calcium carbonate in sea water to make shells. Compound corals join together to build small reefs which are sometimes preserved as massive fossilised structures within limestone rock beds.

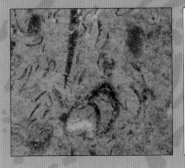

41

Hole of Horcum and Levisham Moor

The Hole of Horcum is the best-known landform on the North York Moors. Every year tens of thousands of walkers are drawn by the huge green bowl that seems to have been scooped out of the surrounding moorland and forest. With heather moorland above and pastures below, the Hole of Horcum gives us clues to the rocks that lie beneath, while the gulleys and streams that flow down its sides give an indication of how it was formed. Just to the west lies the Levisham estate, a unique landscape owned and managed by the Park Authority, which also owes its character to the underlying geology.

This view of the Hole of Horcum shows the different types of vegetation on the slopes. On the left (the eastern side) the upper slopes are covered in trees. This area is underlain by Lower Calcareous Grit. Beneath this is a zone of pasture land which sits on top of Oxford Clay. On the other side, the tops and slopes have been cultivated differently. Here the grit on the top has been used for heather moorland, regularly burned off to bring new shoots – and to prevent the growth of tree cover. The lower slopes are a mix of heather and invasive bracken. The floor of the Hole of Horcum is underlain by Oxford Clay and Osgodby sandstone. On the west side of the beck these have been developed as moorland in contrast to the pastures on the east side.

Hidden among the heather, bracken and trees on the upper slopes are a series of deep gullies, or griffs, that carry water down to the beck below. A large gulley on the north slope is visible in the photograph (below). Although difficult to see from above, the griffs are obvious to anyone walking down the slopes of the Hole of Horcum and these are the key to its formation. As water soaks through the calcareous sandstone on the tops it reaches the next layer of rock, which is the Oxford Clay. The clay is impervious to water, and so the water finds its way out as a series of springs at the junction of the two rocks. These spring waters cut deep gullies in the soft clay, particularly after heavy rainfall. And as the clay is eaten away the overlying grit breaks off in pieces. The Hole of Horcum has formed as a result of these springs operating over many thousands of years. There are similar gullies on the north-facing slope overlooking Saltergate.

On this geology map the Hole of Horcum shows up as a bowl with a long neck. The lower layers of Oxford Clay and Osgodby Sandstone appear as rings. Just to the north is Saltergate Brow and beyond that the moorland. To the west is Levisham Moor and Newtondale.

Newtondale

Saltergate Brow

HOLE OF HORCUM

LEVISHAM MOOR

☐ Lower Calcareous Grit
☐ Oxford Clay
☐ Osgodby Sandstone

By permission of the British Geological Survey

Dundale Griff

Dundale Griff (above) at the south end of Levisham Moor has been cut by waters draining off Levisham Moor down to Levisham Beck in the bottom of the Hole of Horcum. While often dry, these griffs can become torrents after heavy rain.

Levisham Moor extends from the Hole of Horcum west to Newtondale. This area contains a unique combination of remains of human habitation, wildlife and vegetation and is legally protected. The moor is part of the geological structure of the Tabular Hills. The photo below shows the two levels of the moor: the upper shelf is Lower Calcareous Grit, while the lower is Osgodby Formation sandstone.

UPPER CALCAREOUS GRIT

This hard gritty sandstone sits near the top of the Upper Jurassic sequence and is one of the youngest rocks in the region. In most places it has been worn away from the tops of the Tabular Hills, leaving isolated patches above Harwood Dale. It is part of a series of Upper Jurassic beds known collectively as the Corallian Group.

Pseudomelania

Pseudomelania is a beautiful slender gastropod, found throughout the Corallian rocks of the Upper Jurassic. Gastropods with their spiral shells are related to present day snails.

Dales of the Tabular Hills

The dales that run south from the high moorland widen out into beautiful green landscapes. But when they reach the Tabular Hills their shape is altered by the change in geology. The beck waters have cut through these hills to create a series of wooded dales that are quite different to the dales further north. Elsewhere the porous limestone hills have few streams, while on the southern fringe of the hills a layer of impervious clay creates springs.

Douthwaite Dale (above) is in effect the southern extension of Farndale, carrying the waters of the River Dove through the Tabular Hills. Here the dale is a narrower valley with wooded slopes. Further south the beck runs into Kirkdale as the dale opens out with the stream slowly meandering along the flat valley floor.

The Dove and the other becks have worn their way through the layers of rock in the Tabular Hills. A typical section through one of these dales (below) shows the layers of rock sloping down to the south. The land roughly follows this dip but has a more shallow slope. This means that anyone walking from north to south along the top of the dale would be walking down hill, but going up the geological succession. This strange paradox works wherever you walk southwards in the Tabular Hills.

Hodge Beck crosses the old Pickering to Helmsley road via a ford at Kirkdale (below). Here the floor of the beck is made of layers of Malton Oolite. The stream is often dry here, as the waters disappear into natural sink holes to feed the aquifer beneath the Vale of Pickering.

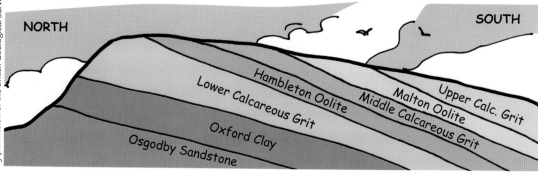

NORTH

SOUTH

Hambleton Oolite

Lower Calcareous Grit

Middle Calcareous Grit

Malton Oolite

Upper Calc. Grit

Oxford Clay

Osgodby Sandstone

By permission of the British Geological Survey

Kirkdale Cave

Near to the Kirkdale ford is a quarry which contains one of the most important sites in the history of geology. In 1821 workmen found hundreds of bones of ice age mammals in the floor of this cave (above). William Buckland analysed the material and suggested that this had been a den for hyenas who dragged the bones back to their lair. This was the beginnings of the new science of palaeontology - not simply reconstructing animals from their remains but working out how they lived.

Outliers

To the north of the Tabular Hills there are some odd cone or barrow-shaped hills. Blakey Topping (right), Howden Hill and Freeborough Hill are outliers from the Tabular Hills – remnants that have stood out against the erosion that has taken away the rocks around them. The first two have a hard cap of Lower Calcareous Grit still sitting on the top, which stops the softer clays underneath being worn away. Freeborough Hill, which is much further north, has a cap of Osgodby sandstone.

Once this layer is worn away the hills will be quickly worn down to the level of the surrounding outliers.

The Bridestones

The Bridestones (above) are a spectacular series of natural sculptures on the edge of Dalby Forest. They are remnants of erosion; pieces of lime-rich rock worn into strange shapes by the effects of wind and rain. The largest is around 10 metres high. The Bridestones are part of a National Trust property that includes Blakey Topping (below) and the escarpment at Crosscliff.

MALTON OOLITE

The Oolite limestones of the Coralline Formation vary from white to yellow to grey in colour, as marine conditions changed throughout the Late Jurassic period.

Perisphinctes

Ammonites are common in the Upper Jurassic marine sediments. *Perisphinctes* thrived in these shallow coral seas.

45

Forge Valley and Hackness

In the far southeast of the National Park lies one of the jewels in the crown of the North York Moors. Forge Valley is a National Nature Reserve, one of the most important mixed woodlands in the north of England, and an enchanting landscape with lots of geological exposures. The valley was cut through the Tabular Hills during and after the last ice age, by water running off from a lake covering present-day Hackness. The lake was held in place by the North Sea ice sheet. When this melted it left behind a bank of mud that diverted streams away from the sea. The Derwent now flows down Forge Valley and through the Vale of Pickering before its waters eventually join the Humber.

The Derwent should really flow eastwards to the sea but has been diverted down Forge Valley by glacial mud. The steep sides of the valley show that it is a recent creation, cut by glacial meltwater. Just as the river flows out of the valley near West Ayton much of its water disappears down through the dipping layers of rock into an underground aquifer. This aquifer is used to supply Scarborough - a town without a river - with its water.

Whetstone quarry (left) is at the north end of Forge Valley high up on the eastern hill side. The Lower Calcareous Grit here is a deep yellow. As the name implies the stone here was quarried for grinding wheels, used for sharpening knives and tools. There is a geological trail that leads through the quarries in the valley; see the Natural England website for details.

Located at the southern end of Forge Valley, Whitestone Quarry (right) is an exposure of Hambleton Oolite, one of the highest beds in the Upper Jurassic succession. Notice the difference in colour between the yellow sandstone and white oolite.

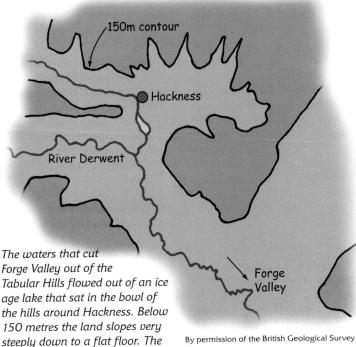

By permission of the British Geological Survey

William Smith, 'The Father of English geology', lived and worked on the Hackness Estate from 1828 to 1834 after which he lived in Scarborough. Smith laid the foundations of English geology by recognising that rock strata could be analysed and dated through the fossils they contained.

The waters that cut Forge Valley out of the Tabular Hills flowed out of an ice age lake that sat in the bowl of the hills around Hackness. Below 150 metres the land slopes very steeply down to a flat floor. The lake was dammed on the eastern side by the North Sea ice sheet, leaving the waters to flow south towards Forge Valley. The Sea Cut was built to relieve flooding.

This map of the surface geology (below) shows the valley cutting down through the Upper Jurassic beds (calcareous grits and oolites) and into the Oxford Clay and Osgodby sandstone beneath.

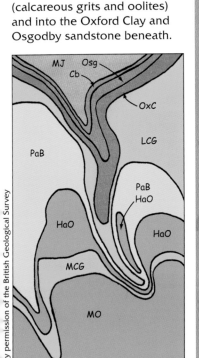

CLOUGHTON SANDSTONE

The Cloughton Formation is part of the Middle Jurassic series of rocks, formed at a time when this region was a coastal delta. Cloughton sandstones were formed in river beds. They are even-grained and were valued as building stone. There are outcrops in the cliffs and scars north of Scarborough and at quarries near Cloughton village.

Unio kendalli
Unio kendalli is a freshwater mussel that lived in the same rivers where the Cloughton sandstone was formed.

Nilsonnia
The Middle Jurassic rocks of Yorkshire are famous for their plant fossils. Conifers, tree ferns, gingkos ferns and cycads, such as this *Nilsonnia* grew across the region. Leaves and stems have been preserved in the sand and mudbanks.

Useful information

We hope this book will encourage you to explore the landscape of the North York Moors National Park. The area has two museums with spectacular displays of local fossils:

Whitby Museum, Pannett Park, Whitby
www.whitbymuseum.org.uk

The Rotunda Geology Museum, Cliff Bridge Terrace, Scarborough
www.rotundamuseum.org.uk

There are lots of places to get further information about the National Park, much of it published by the National Park Authority. The main National Park Visitor Centres are at:

Sutton Bank National Park Centre
01845 597426

The Moors National Park Centre, Danby
01439 772737

The North York Moors National Park website is at www.northyorkmoors.org.uk

Further reading
Rocks and Landscape of the North York Moors is one of a short series of illustrated books about the National Park. The others are:

Roger Osborne and Alistair Bowden (2001) *The Dinosaur Coast: Yorkshire Rocks, Reptiles and Landscape*, North York Moors National Park Authority

Roger Osborne (2006) *Discover the North York Moors*, North York Moors National Park Authority

For a more technical book about the geology of the coast try:

Peter F Rawson and John K Wright (2000) *Geologists' Association Guide to the Yorkshire Coast*, Geologists' Association

The British Geological Survey publishes geological maps of the area, available for purchase via their website. Some maps can be viewed online. Visit www.bgs.ac.uk

Some books about the landscape and flora of the area and its history:

D A Spratt and B J D Harrison (editors) (1989) *The North York Moors Landscape Heritage*, North York Moors National Park Authority

Robin A Butlin (editor) and Nick Staley (2003) *Historical Atlas of North Yorkshire*, Westbury

Nan Sykes (2004) *Wildflowers of the North Yorkshire Coast*, North York Moors National Park Authority